and The Cub Scout 'SU...

CONTENTS

THE FOLLOWING IS A GUIDE ONLY

● BEAVER ITEM   ● CUB ITEM   ● BEAVER AND CUB ITEM

CUB AND BEAVER SCOUT
ANNUAL 2001

Pedigree®

Published by Pedigree Books Limited
The Old Rectory, Matford Lane, Exeter   EX2 4PS

£6.99

CODE BREAKERS!

When you walk in the country, you follow the Country Code. When you ride your bike through town, you obey the Highway Code. Now its time to learn the special Beaver and Cub Scout Annual code!

For the first time, The Beaver Scout and Cub Scout Annual have combined to make one exciting, bumper book. Some of the stories and features are of special interest to Beaver readers. Others are aimed at older Cub readers. And some items are of general interest to any Scout and appeal to both groups. So how do you tell which is which?

EASY! IT'S COLOUR CODED

GREEN FOR BEAVER

Pages which have this colour edge are of particular interest to Beavers. the material is linked to the aims and objectives of The Beaver Scouts.

BLUE FOR CUB

This colour edge indicates that these pages are especially for Cubs. Many of these items are closely linked to gaining Award Badges. **Please Note** They are just there to give ideas to help towards gaining your badge. You cannot actually gain any of the badges by just reading or using the activities! Please refer to The Cub Scout Handbook for full badge requirements.

GREEN AND BLUE

As you might expect, when both colours merge together the items on these pages appeal to both Beaver and Cubs. These items are not affected by the difference in age between the two Scout Groups.

AND FINALLY

Your new double annual is interesting, exciting and fun –

SO WHY NOT READ IT!

THE THREE BEAVERS IN HORSEY, HORSEY!

Baz and Sharon were going horseriding. Lucy, their friend from the Beaver Scout Colony, had asked them to feed and exercise her pony, Bubbles, while she was on holiday.

Daz saw his Beaver chums setting off for the stables. "Please may I come with you?" he called, eagerly. "I'd love to ride a horse." "All right then," agreed Baz and Sharon, kindly.

Under the watchful eye of the Beaver Scout Leader, Baz and Sharon rode Bubbles round and round the paddock. "My turn now!" whooped Daz, almost bursting with excitement.

The little beaver was so keen to start riding that he took a flying leap onto Bubbles' back. "Look out!" yelled Baz, as Darren jumped right over the pony and landed on top of him!

At last, Daz managed to clamber into the saddle. But he mounted Bubbles back to front! "W-W-What's happened?" he cried in dismay. "Someone's stolen the horse's head!"

Finally, the youngster started to ride. But he pretended to be a cowboy and shouted "Yahoo!" Bubbles threw him off and he landed in a muddy puddle - squirting poor Sharon in the face!

THERE ARE SIX HORSESHOES HIDDEN IN THIS PICTURE

CAN YOU FIND THEM ALL?

11

BODY LANGUAGE

"Shall I just put an 'S' on th end of that long word? It's the easiest way to get loads of points!"

Photo: Roy Bushby

"Oh, come on, will you? How long does take to cook a gooey little pancake

Photo: David G

"This looked easy when the bloke did it he had six on the go at one time!"

Photo: David Gartan

PHOTOGRAPHER BADGE

12

"The best way to
escape the
washing up is in the
washing bowl!"

Photo: Ron Golds

"One smart crack from
you and this lot's going
right over your head!"

Photo: Iris Brooks

13

IF YOU GO DOWN TO THE WOODS TODAY...

Oh, dear! Baz and Sharon have gone orienteering with their Beaver Colony... and Daz has followed them! Now the little beaver is lost and all alone!

Help poor Daz to rejoin his friends by finding the one path that leads right through the woods.

So you'd like to know how to make . . .

A FISHING GAME

like to make things

Here's a step-by-step guide how to make it . . .

How do you fancy a fishing trip where you don't get cold or wet and you're certain to catch lots of fish after only a few moments? Well, it can all come true - if you make yourself this big fun, mini fishing game…

WARNING Scissors are sharp and dangerous. Ask a grown-up to do the cutting-out for you, or make sure one is nearby when you do it yourself.

ARTIST BADGE

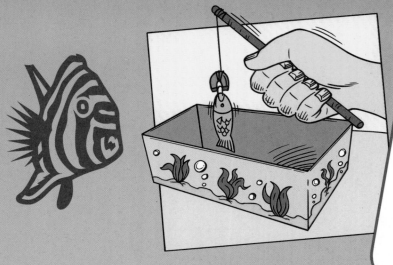

THINGS YOU NEED

- **Several strips of thin cardboard** (different colours if possible)
- **Pencil**
- **Scissors** (children's safety scissors are best)
- **Felt pens**
- **Some paper clips**
- **Thin wooden gardening sticks**
- **Some thin string**
- **A small horseshoe magnet** (more if you want several rods)

1. Using the pencil, draw the outline of a fish on each strip of cardboard. Your fish can be all different sizes and shapes.

2. Carefully cut out each fish, throwing away the unwanted scraps of cardboard.

3. Using the felt pens, colour and decorate your fish shapes in any way you wish.

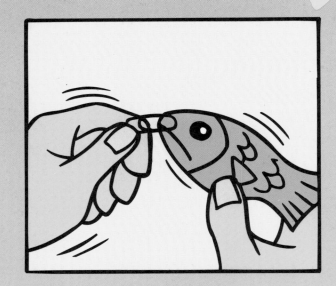

4. Now take each fish in turn and gently push a paper-clip onto its nose. This is made of metal, so the fish will be picked up by the magnet.

5. To make your fishing rod - cut a short length of string and tie one end to the top of the wooden stick. Tie the other end of the string to the magnet. (Do this two or three times if you have enough magnets for everyone to have their own fishing line.)

6. Finally, arrange your fish in the bottom of a shallow box or on a tray. (You can decorate the box to look like a pond if you wish). Then hover the magnet over the fish and - hey presto - you'll find yourself catching them one after another!

8. To make your fishing game into a competition, just write different numbers onto the back of each fish. Then, when they have all been caught, you can add up your total scores and the person with the highest is the **winner!**

WoW!

WHAT'S

WRONG?

This picture of Baz, Daz and Sharon out for a cycle ride contains ten silly mistakes. Can you spot them all?

WHICH WITCH IS WHICH?

Jane has dressed up as a witch to go to the Cub Pack Fancy Dress Party. Look carefully at these six pictures of here in her outfit. Only two are exactly the same. Can you spot the matching pair?

ANSWER Pictures 1 and 5 are the same

THE SUPER SIX IN "EVERYBODY'S GONE SURFIN'!"

"Do I look mega-cool?"asked Ice. "Or do I look mega'cool?" "You look okay," replied Joe.

"Okay?" exclaimed Ice, lifting his dark glasses in disgust. "Look again, bone-brain!"

"I'm not a bone-brain!" retorted Joe. "Gus is!"

"My brain's not made of bone… is it?" murmured Gus, frowning. "Oh, brother!" exclaimed Ice, striking his head with his hand. "What am I doing here with you two twits?"

"I'm not your brother… am I?" added Gus.

SWIMMER BADGE

COMPUTER BADGE

The three Cub Scouts were standing outside the local swimming pool. Ice was holding his prize possession - a full-size surfboard. "Surfing's one of the coolest things you can do!" boasted Ice. "And I'm gonna do some right now." "How can you?" cried Joe. "It's the wrong time of year for starters - and we're miles from the sea." "I have my ways," chuckled Ice, turning on his heel and marching into the swimming pool.

The pool had a wave-making machine in it and Ice was best friends with Dave, the attendant in charge of it. "I can't wait," chuckled Ice, hurrying to get changed. "Dave's going to put the wave-making machine up to maximum so I get some roller for surfing!" Soon, Ice was in the water with his surfboard. He waved to Dave up in the control-room and his friend turned the wave-maker to full power. "This is gonna be so cool!" chuckled Ice.

Brenda, Jane and Sammy were already in the pool. The girls were helping Sammy to practice for his Swimming Badge.

"Keep going, Sam!" urged Jane. "You've nearly swum a whole length!" The trio were so busy splashing about in the water that they did not notice the first big wave surging towards them. Only when it towered above their heads did they react.

"Look out!" yelled Brenda, her words getting drowned by the mighty! "WHOOSH"! as the wave broke over them. They had to cling onto the rails for dear life to prevent themselves being sucked back by the undertow - only to find another gigantic roller frothing towards them.

Ice was waiting on the low diving-board. As the wave passed him, he leapt forwards on his surfboard and rode the crest like a true surfer. Then he lost his balance.

"Wipe-out!" he yelled, turning head over heels in the curving wave. Sammy and the girls were still scrambling up the concrete beach when Ice and his surfboard hit them. "OWW! .. URRGH! ..ARRGH!" they all yelled. "How can I possibly become a champion surfer when you lot keep getting in my way?" Shouted Ice.

Still trying to look cool, Ice went back for another ride. By now, the wave-machine was at full power, producing tidal waves that were too big for the pool. Ice caught one and surfed powerfully across the pool - only to find that the wave was to big, it was going out the double doors!

SCOOOOOOSH!

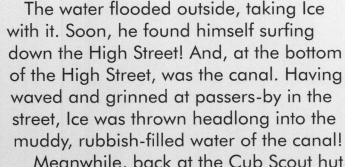

The water flooded outside, taking Ice with it. Soon, he found himself surfing down the High Street! And, at the bottom of the High Street, was the canal. Having waved and grinned at passers-by in the street, Ice was thrown headlong into the muddy, rubbish-filled water of the canal!

Meanwhile, back at the Cub Scout hut, Gus and Joe were checking out the new computer that the Pack had just bought. "It's brill!" exclaimed Joe, working the keypad. "We've got full access to the internet."

Just then, Sammy and the two girls arrived home from the swimming pool. They soon forgot about Ice's antics when they saw the new computer. "Let's put it through its paces," cried Sammy, excitely. "See what it can do!"

Everyone was busy on the computer when Ice arrived back at the hut. He looked far from cool now. He was all muddy from the canal and had assorted bits of junk clinging to his clothes. "Fancy a spot of surfing, Ice?" called Joe. "Funny guy!" snapped Ice. "No, we mean it," laughed Gus. "We're surfin' the net! It's the coolest thing you can do nowadays!" In fact, the computer was turned off for the next five minutes - everyone was too busy laughing at the sick look on Ice's face!"

have fun

JUST FOR FUN!

KNOCK, KNOCK!
Who's there?
AMANDA!
Amanda who?
AMANDA fix the washing machine!

What is small, round, crunchy and giggles a lot?
A TICKLED ONION!

I SAY, WAITER! THERE'S A SPIDER IN MY SOUP!
I KNOW, SIR. THE FLY IS ON HOLIDAY!

Say this several times as fast as you can -
PURPLE PEOPLE-EATER

What did the first magnet say to the second magnet?
I find you so attractive!

What do you call a baby whale?
A Little Squirt!

WHAT FALLS ALL DAY BUT NEVER GETS HURT?
A WATERFALL!

ENTERTAINER BADGE

TONGUE-TWISTERS TO MAKE YOUR FRIENDS GROAN!

DOCTOR, DOCTOR!
I keep thinking I'm an orange!
HAVE YOU TRIED PLAYING SQUASH?

What did the boy octopus say to the girl octopus?
I want to hold your hand, your hand, your hand ...

WHERE DOES A SHEEP GO TO GET ITS HAIR CUT?
A BAA BAA SHOP!

iF YOUR NOSE RUNS AND YOUR FEET SMELL, YOU'RE UPSIDE DOWN!

A woman rushed into a DIY shop and said:
"I'd like a mousetrap, please. And can you be quick - I've got a bus to catch."
"Sorry, madam," replied the shop assistant.
"We don't sell mousetraps that BiG!".

What kind of mistakes do ghosts make?
Boo-Boos!

NICK NACK PADDY-WHACK, give the dog a... HOME!

If you and your family are looking for a dog, why not adopt one of the thousands of strays that are cared for by the NCDL (The National Canine Defence League)...

NOT JUST FOR CHRISTMAS

People often give dogs as presents, especially at Christmas. When their new owners realise their pet needs regular feeding and walks, many don't want the trouble. So they do a dreadful thing - they let the dog go free to look after itself. This is very upsetting and dangerous for the dog and many get hurt. But fortunately the NCDL is there to help stray and abandoned dogs and to help them find a new home with kind owners who will look after them all of their lives.

Karen Marr with Scrappy from the NCDL Rehoming Centre in West Calder   Photograph by Jason Venus

Al and Bonnie, two border collies from the NCDL Rehoming Centre at Bridgend in South Wales.   Photograph by Jason Venus

NCDL's 1999 poster campaign, celebrating their 21st anniversary for their famous slogan: " IS FOR LIFE, NOT JUST FOR CHRISTMAS"
Photograph by Vicki Couchman

THE NCDL, PAST AND PRESENT

The NCDL began in 1891 at the first-ever Crufts Dog Show in London. A kind-hearted lady called Gertrude Stock formed a small group of wealthy people who promised to spend their time and money fighting against cruelty to dogs. In the next century, they and their followers helped make many changes in the law which gave dogs a better life. Today, the NCDL cares for over 12,000 unwanted dogs. And those that cannot be rehomed are looked after by caring staff at one of the 15 Rehoming Centres around the country. The NDCL never destroys healthy dogs in its care. Those that nobody want live at their Rehoming Centre all their lives, or until a new home can be found.

WHAT TO DO IF YOU FIND A STRAY

Never approach a stray dog on your own - always find a grown-up to help you. See if the animal is wearing a disc. The law says every dog should have its owner's name and address on its collar, so you may be able to find out where it comes from by that. If not, you should contact or take the dog to:

- the local police station
- the local dog warden
- a nearby vet (if it needs medical help)
- the nearest NCDL Rehoming Centre

WHAT TO DO IF YOU WANT TO ADOPT A DOG

Every NCDL Rehoming Centre had hundreds of dogs looking for new homes. So you and your family can phone up your nearest branch and make an appointment to view them. A member of staff will advise you about each dog and help you to choose the one that is most suitable to your needs. A pre-adoption visit will be made to your home to make sure the dog will be happy and safe there. And, if this proves okay, your parents sign some papers and you take your new pet home!

For further information, please write to:

The NCDL, 17 Wakley Street, LONDON EC1V 7HQ or ring the Rehoming Hotline: 0345 646000 or visit the NCDL's website: www.ncdl.org.uk

Information and photographs kindly supplied by NCDL

Molly, Tam and Shep enjoy the dogs' adventure playground at the NCDL Rehoming Centre in Shoreham, Sussex.
Photograph by Jason Venus

GENERAL KNOWLEDGE QUESTIONS SPECIALLY FOR BEAVER SCOUTS...

1 In the nursery rhyme, how many men did the Grand Old Duke Of York march to the top of the hill?

One hundred

One thousand

Ten thousand

2 In which capital city would you find the Eiffel Tower?

London

Paris

Rome

3 Baby rabbits are called "kittens".

TRUE?   FALSE?

4 Complete this sentence -

You make the colour mauve by mixing together the colours R- - and B - - -.

5 Whose best friend and right-hand man was called Little John?

Robin Hood

King Arthur

Big John

6 What is the largest living animal in the world?

Bull elephant

Blue whale

Beaver in a fish factory

7 What is the fastest land animal in the world?

Cheetah

Tortoise

Beaver chased by a wolf

8 Rearrange these scrambled-up letters to spell the name of the Queen's house in London -

NCHMAGIUBK Palace

9 Which country invented curry?

India

China

Iceland

10 Beaversaurus was a small, noisy, very active dinosaur that liked to meet in groups.

TRUE? FALSE?

11 If you were a plumber, what sort of work would you do?

Pick plums

Work at a swimming club

Fix water pipes

12 In which part of your body would you find your spine?

Your back

Your leg

Your head

SHARON'S
COOL
Computer Code

Sharon and Baz want to surprise Darren by inviting him to their Beaver Colony for a day. To stop the eager little Beaver finding out the date, Sharon sent an e-mail to Baz in code.
Can you break the code? Just look at each number in turn and write the letter it stands for underneath. Then you will spell out Darren's special day!

1	A
2	B
3	C
4	D
5	E
6	F
7	G
8	H
9	I
10	J
11	K
12	L
13	M
14	N
15	O
16	P
17	Q
18	R
19	S
20	T
21	U
22	V
23	W
24	X
25	Y
26	Z

1 16 18 9 12   20 8 5
–   –   –   –   –   –   –   –

20 23 5 14 20 25
 –   –   –   –   –   –

20 8 9 18 4, 19 1 9 14 20
 –   –   –   –   – , –   –   –   –   –

7 5 15 18 7 5'19   4 1 25
–   –   –   –   –   – ' –   –   –   –

Baz Goes Shopping

At home, Baz was building a home-made cart when his Mum asked him to go shopping. "We need some fish for tea," she said. Baz wanted to keep working, but he knew it was his duty as a Beaver to be helpful. "Okay, Mum," he said.

Baz was just setting off for the shops when he had an idea. "Why don't I do the shopping in my new cart?" he chuckled, jumping in. He rolled away, happy to be doing what he wanted and what his Mum wanted.

31

At first, the trip went well. Then Baz found himself speeding down a hill, so he tried to put on the brakes. "Arrgh!" he yelled in dismay, "I haven't put brakes on my cart yet!"

Baz hurtled down the hill, getting faster and faster by the minute. The road let to a river. "I'm going to get w-w-wet!" wailed Baz, as he thundered into the water with a huge splash.

"Hey! I'm floating!" laughed Baz, as his home-made cart bobbed around at the edge of the river like a boat. But the Beaver's smile did not last long. "Gaah! Now I'm sinking" he yelled.

Being a Beaver, Baz was an expert swimmer - and he was only in the shallows by the riverbank. Coughing and spluttering, he scrambled out of the water, pulling his cart behind him.

Squelch, Squelch, Squelch! Baz walked home, dripping wet. "Oh, no!" he gasped, as he reached his front gate. "After all that, I still haven't done Mum's shopping. She wanted fish for tea."

In fact, Mum did get her fish for tea! You see, Baz had caught one when he pulled his cart out of the river. "What a bit of luck!" laughed Baz. "I've been a good Beaver today after all!"

So you'd like to know how to make . . .

MUSICAL SHAKERS

SHAKE, RATTLE AND ROLL!

You can add an extra rhythm line to your favourite CD by making these colourful shakers (whose correct musical name is maracas)…

Here's how you can make them!

WARNING There is nothing dangerous in this make, but it does involve the use of PVA glue and poster paint. These are very messy, so make sure you wear something to protect your clothes and that a grown-up knows you might need help.

MUSICIAN BADGE

THINGS YOU NEED

- Two washing-up liquid bottles (tall, cylinder shape)
- Some dried peas
- Some rice
- A small plastic funnel
- Two short pieces of round wooden dowling
- Some white PVA glue
- Poster paints
- Strong sticky tape

1. Remove the nozzle from the first washing-up bottle and pour a small quantity of dried peas into the bottle - enough to make a loud sound when shaken about. (Very important - spilt dried peas go everywhere!)

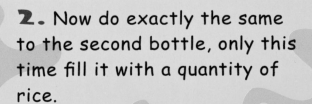

2. Now do exactly the same to the second bottle, only this time fill it with a quantity of rice.

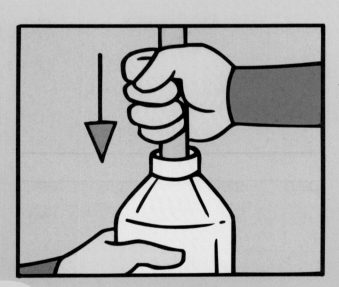

3. Take each bottle in turn and brush some white PVA glue into the hole at the top. Then take the wooden dowling sticks and push them into the holes. Make sure it is a nice, tight fit. Allow to dry.

4. To further strengthen the join between your plastic bottles and their new wooden handles, wind two or three loops of sticky tape around both of them. (Now your maracas won't fall apart when you shake them!

5. Now it's time to decorate your shakers. So that the poster paints will stick to the plastic bottles, it needs to be mixed with some PVA glue. You will have to do this for every colour you wish to use.

PAINT YOUR SHAKERS IN ANY WAY YOU WISH

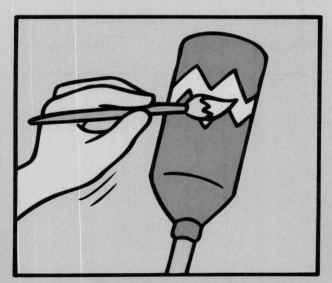

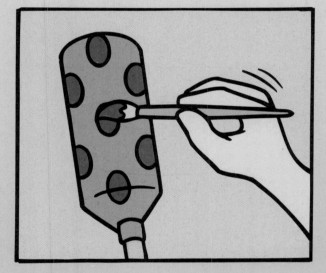

6. One idea is to paint both of them with a different plain colour like yellow and blue. Then, to make it clear that one shaker contains rice and the other contains dried peas, decorate the first with a zig-zag pattern...

7. ...and the second with big, colourful circles. Allow to dry before you start playing your maracas - otherwise you'll shake paint all over everyone!

BEAUTiFUL BALLOONS

SUMMER FAYRE

ARTIST BADGE

Brenda and Jane are selling balloons at their Cub Scout Pack Summer Fayre. Make this picture as colourful as you can with your pencil crayons or felt-tip pens.

try new things

ACTION SCOUTS!

"This feels like being on 'You've Been Frame WAAAHH!"

Photo: John Fogg

"I wouldn't be grinning like this if the glider was up in the air!"

Photo: Chris Boardman

"Now I know what you meant when you said you were roping people in for the obstacle course!"

Photo: Chris Boardman

"It's not that we're lazy or anything, it's just that we don't believe in exerting ourselves!"

Photo: John Fogg

"No, I'm serious. I'm telling you I'm stuck!"

THE BiG TENNIS "MATCH"

Gus and Joe want to play tennis, but their equipment is all in a muddle. Can you help them to sort it out?

By drawing a line or just tracing with your finger, match the five pairs of tennis stuff. When you have finished, there will be one item left over. Can you name the odd-one-out?

The True Tale Of ...
GREYFRIARS BOBBY

Edinburgh, the capital of Scotland, has a fine castle which towers over the city below. Edinburgh Castle still stands today, unlike the jumble of dirty buildings which used to shelter beneath its walls over a hundred and fifty years ago. These have long-since been pulled down and their poor, hard-working owners forgotten - with the exception of one old shepherd and his loyal, loving dog…

The old buildings beneath the Castle were known as Greyfriars. Every week, for as long as anyone could remember, Old Jock had visited the market that was held there to buy food and clothes. For most of his seventy years, he had been alone. Recently, however, the shepherd who worked in the surrounding hills had been accompanied by a little Skye terrier called Bobby. The dog, who lived on a local farm, had befriended Old Jock and went everywhere with him. The old man loved his new friend's energy and mischief!

BOOK READERS
BADGE

One misty morning, as Old Jock trudged to the market as usual, Bobby spotted a rabbit in Greyfriars Churchyard. With a yelp of delight, the lively terrier charged after the rabbit, much to the annoyance of Mr Brown, the church caretaker.

"Come out of there, you wee scoundrel!" shouted Mr Brown, chasing Bobby round the paths of the churchyard. "Dogs are not allowed in here." Eventually, Bobby returned to Old Jock and hid behind his legs.

"I promise you, Mr Brown," said the elderly shepherd, "Bobby will never set foot in your churchyard again."

Old Jock kept his word…for as long as he was alive. For the old man was growing slower and more tired with each passing day and he had a dreadful cough which kept him awake most of the night. One winters night, when the snow lay thick on the ground and a bitter wind blew across the silent, white hills, Old Jock died. Bobby was by his side, licking his master's face and nuzzling his hand in an attempt to revive him.

A few days later, the shepherd was buried in the churchyard he had passed so often on his way to market. Mr Brown was there to pay his last respects, as were all the shabbily-dressed folk from Greyfriars who had lost their oldest friend. When the funeral was over and the small crowd dispersed, a familiar figure wriggled under the church gate and sat on Old Jock's grave. It was Bobby! Of course, Mr Brown did not want him to stay there and chased him away. But every time the caretaker's back was turned, Bobby would return to sit on Old Jock's grave. The dog sat upright and alert, waiting for any sign of his beloved master's return.

A few days later, a cart drew up at the churchyard gates and the farmer who had once owned Bobby marched in and caught the dog. Bobby was taken back to the farm which was out in the country, several miles from Edinburgh. But even though he was loved and well fed in his new home, Bobby escaped and ran all the way back to the city to resume his lonely vigil on Old Jock's grave!

It seemed that nothing would stop Bobby from living in the churchyard. So Mr Brown and the elders of Greyfriars Church gave in and allowed him to stay. Mr Brown's daughter, Jennie, was given the job of feeding the little dog which she did faithfully for many years to come. Greyfriars Bobby, as the terrier came to be known, soon became a tourist attraction and the people of Edinburgh would flock to see the famous dog.

Living outside in all weathers took its toll on Bobby, just as it had done on his master. One autumn evening, Jennie Brown found Bobby lying motionless on top of his master's gravestone. Bobby was buried beside his master and a bronze sign was put up in his memory.

"I wish everyone loved each other like Greyfriars Bobby loved Old Jock," murmured Jennie.

WHAT'S FOR TEA TONIGHT?

Young Sammy is at his first Cub Scout Camp and all the outdoor activities are making him EXTRA hungry!

Sammy likes all the camp food, but you can find out his very favourite by fitting these names into the grid, using the letters already in place to guide you. When you have finished, the middle section reading downwards will spell out what he likes best.

BEANS
CORNFLAKES
APPLES
SAUSAGES
CHICKEN
BREAD
CAKE
BANANAS

COOK BADGE

CAMPER BADGE

ANSWER Sammy's favourite tea is pancakes.

COMPETITION TIME

Beavers go on visits

Last year's Beaver Annual and Cub Annual Competitions were both huge successes. Thousands of you sent in your entries, hoping to win that wonderful prize of a free trip to Butlins for your Beaver Colony or your Cub Pack. Details of the two lucky winners are on the following pages. Then comes news of this year's fantastic prizes - a free Colony visit and a free Pack visit to a Sea Life Centre near you! Finally, there's this year's competition question. (It's not difficult!) So, if you didn't win last year, why not try again this year. As they say for that other lesser competition

It could be you...

NATURALIST BADGE

ANIMAL LOVERS BADGE

WIN ONE OF THESE TWO SUPER PRIZES

A Beaver Colony Visit To A Sea Life Centre or A Cub Pack Visit To A Sea Life Centre (Both for up to 30 children and 6 accompanying adults)

NOW PLAYING AT A SEA LIFE CENTRE NEAR YOU...

There's a whole new world of adventure and wonder just waiting to be discovered beneath the waves. Sea Life Centres take visitors on an incredible voyage into this mysterious world, bringing them closer than they imagined possible to sharks, rays and a host of other marine life.

If you're one of the two lucky winners of this year's competition, you and all your Beaver Colony or Cub Pack friends, plus six grown-ups, can visit the Sea Life Centre nearest you absolutely free. Thanks to the generosity of Merlin Entertainments, you'll have a day out to remember for a lifetime!

ALL SIMILAR, YET ALL DIFFERENT

Each of the Centres dotted around the British cost, plus the National Sea Life Centre in Birmingham, is teeming with its own special characters and displays. Many feature exciting underwater "walkthrough" tunnels which allow you literally to walk along the seabed! And the Centres at Scarborough and Oban

48

have the added interest of special seal rescue departments.

The Sea Life Centres taking part in this Beaver Competition 2001 are as follows:

Weymouth Sea Life Park
Brighton Sea Life Centre
Great Yarmouth Sea Life Centre
National Sea Life Centre, Birmingham
Blackpool Sea Life Centre
National Seal Sanctury, Cornwall
Oban Seal And Marine Centre, Scotland
Scarborough Seal and Marine Centre

The winners will choose the most convenient centre to visit from this list.

THE UNDERWATER WORLD - INDOORS!

All the Sea Life Centres pride themselves on recreating in their tanks the many and varied underwater habitats found around our coastline. Every display holds a stunning variety of wildlife which lives in a particular enviroment– such as the shifting sands of a rivermouth or the freezing water of the deep ocean. And each Centre pays close attention

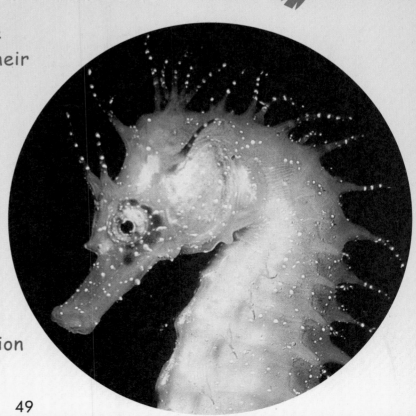

to their local area, making realistic backdrops to the tanks that closely mirror the surrounding coastline.

HANDS-ON EXPERIENCE

The Sea Life Centres understand very well that children don't just like to see things, they like to touch them and feel them in close-up. So special SeaLab areas let you get to grips with creatures like sturdy crabs and starfish. Within the Labs, there are also "nursery units" which are filled with baby sharks and rays as they hatch out of their see-through egg-cases.

ALL THINGS TO ALL MEN

The network of Sea Life Centres around the country do a number of jobs, all of which are very important. As well as giving their visitors an exciting and fun day out, they are spreading knowledge and teaching everyone about the wonderful world of the sea. This educational role is supported by special talks, feeding displays and demonstrations which appeal to the whole family. Sea Life Centres are closely involved with the environment and see themselves as guardians of the sea at a time when the need to protect our fragile world has never been so important. And many Sea-Life Centres run their own breeding programmes as well as

rescuing sick or injured sea animals, making them better and releasing them back into the wild.

AND THAT'S NOT ALL...

EXCITING NEWS OF TWO SPECIAL OFFERS JUST FOR SCOUTS -

If you're not lucky enough to win this year's competition and get your Beaver Colony or Cub Pack into a Sea Life Centre absolutely free, you can still make a visit at a reduced rate. Each Sea Life Centre has a special entry rate for Scouts, such as one free place for every 10 paying to enter. For further details, call at your local Sea Life Centre or telephone 01202 440022.

INTRODUCING...

The Sea Life Cub Scout Challenge & Adventure Pack!
New for 2000 is a specially designed Cub Scout pack full of brilliant ideas and activities and it's free with each booking to a Sea Life Centre. The pack includes marine links for work towards badges and also has some great ideas for activity days. With tests and challenges, the pack will prove a valuable resource both for visits to Sea Life and for use again and again on marine based activities in the future.

Photographs and information kindly supplied by Merlin Entertainments

COMPETITION QUESTIONS

Hammerhead, Tiger and Great White are all types of what?

WHALES

SHARKS

RAYS

If you think you know the correct answer, write it down on the entry form on the next page. Then, in the space provided, say what you enjoy most about being a Beaver Scout or being a Cub Scout. Finally, fill in all the information about yourself.

The completed entry form needs to be cut out and sent in. (If you don't want to spoil your annual, please feel free to photocopy the form.) Send your entry to:

> Beaver Scout and Cub Scout Annual 2001 Competition
> The Scout Association, Baden-Powell House
> Queen's Gate, London SW7 5JS

(And please don't forget to put a stamp on your envelope. The Post Office will not deliver any unstamped entries.)

CLOSING DATE FOR COMPETITION: WEDNESDAY FEBRUARY 28 2001.

After this closing date, all the correct entries will be put in a hat (well, it's a big box actually - a hat wouldn't be big enough!) and shaken about. Then one form will be selected completely at random. The lucky winner will be informed by post and details published in the Beaver and Cub Annual 2002.

BEAVER SCOUT AND CUB SCOUT ANNUAL 2001 COMPETITION

Hammerhead, Tiger and Great White are all types of:

_____

What I enjoy most about being a Beaver Scout/Cub Scout (delete as required) is (no more than 20 words):

_____

_____

_____

_____

_____

My name is: _____   My age is: _____

My home address is: _____

_____

_____

My Beaver Colony/Cub Pack is: _____

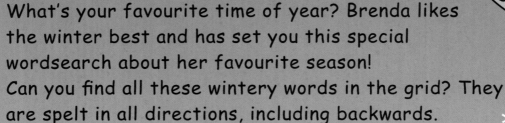

WINTER WORDSEARCH

What's your favourite time of year? Brenda likes the winter best and has set you this special wordsearch about her favourite season!
Can you find all these wintery words in the grid? They are spelt in all directions, including backwards.

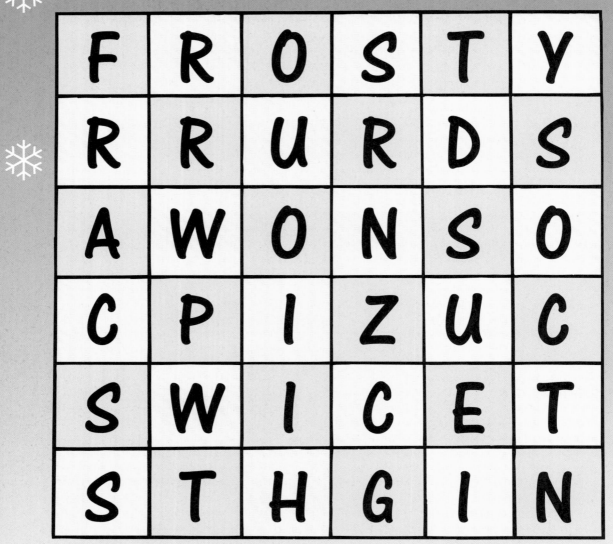

F	R	O	S	T	Y
R	R	U	R	D	S
A	W	O	N	S	O
C	P	I	Z	U	C
S	W	I	C	E	T
S	T	H	G	I	N

SCARF   FROZEN   SPORT   FROSTY
ICE   NIGHTS   RUN   WINDY
SNOW   COSY   NUT

OBSERVATION
SKILLS

54

THE SUPER SIX IN
A STITCH IN TIME

SPORTSMAN BADGE

HOBBIES BADGE

56

58

There are six cotton reels hidden in the picture. Can you find them all?

59

PHOTO FUN

"There's one sausage left on the barbeque. Do you reckon anyone would miss it?"

Photo: Chris Boardman

"Hi, guys! This is my toothpas[te] advert smil[e]"

Photo: Chris Boardman

"That's as far as I'm going. This tyre is full of foul green smelly water!"

Photo: Chris Boardman

"They don't expect us to climb that, do they?"

"Do I have to wear this hat, Mum? I'm really not sure about it!"

61

Racing Roadsters

Can you spot six small differences between these two pictures of
Ice racing his remote-controlled car round the park?

OBSERVATION
SKILLS

So you'd like to know how to make . . .

ROCK CAKES

try new things

YUMMY...YUMMY... SCRUMMY ROCK CAKES!

They're crunchy on the outside, soft and fluffy on the inside and they smell delicious!

The following pages show you how to make some of your own. If you follow each step carefully, you can't go wrong - this is a foolproof recipe tried and tested at countless Beaver Colony and Cub Pack meetings...

WARNING Using the kitchen - especially a hot oven - can be dangerous. You must have a grown-up with you at all times!

COOK'S BADGE

KITCHEN ITEMS YOU NEED

- Mixing bowl
- Wooden spoon
- Sieve
- Baking tray
- Oven gloves

INGREDIENTS

225g self-raising flour
100g margarine
75g caster sugar
75g dried mixed fruit
1 egg
2-3 tablespoons milk
pinch of salt

1. Put the flour into the sieve and add the pinch of salt. Then shake gently so that all the flour and salt drops into the mixing bowl underneath. (This has separated all the grains and put some air into the mixture to make it light.)

2. Cut the margarine into chunks and put it into the bowl. Then, with your fingers, mix the margarine with the flour and salt. When you have finished, the mixture should look like fine breadcrumbs.

3. Crack the egg and drop it into the mixture. Add the sugar. Add the dried mixed fruit.

4. Mix all the ingredients together, adding no more than two tablespoons of milk to make it mix easily. Your finished dough should be quite stiff and hard to stir.

5. Wipe your baking tray with the margarine wrapper to make it slightly greasy. (This stops the finished rock cakes from sticking) Then cover the tray with small heaps of the mixture until it is all used up.

DELICIOUS!

6. Finally, preheat the oven to 220 C and cook for 15-20 minutes until golden. Cool before eating. As a final touch, you can sprinkle the tops of your rock cakes with sugar for extra taste!

BEAVER

GENERAL KNOWLEDGE QUESTIONS SPECIALLY FOR CUB SCOUTS...

1 In which year did The Titanic hit the iceberg and sink?

a) 1812

b) 1912

c) 2012

2 What is a 'clone'?

a) A funny man at a circus

b) A red and white plastic shape used on motorways

c) A copy of a living creature made by scientists

3 Can you complete this sentence?

"John Lennon, Paul McCartney, Ringo Starr and George Harrison were better known as _____ _____."

4 How does an octopus defend itself against attack?

a) It squirts out a jet of black 'ink'

b) It hits out with all its eight legs

c) It sticks out its tongue and shouts 'Go away!'

5 In America, the bonnet of a car is called the 'trunk' and the boot is called the 'hood'.

True? False?

6 What is a coral reef made of?

a) Rocks formed by underwater volcanoes

b) The bones of millions of tiny sea creatures

c) Candy floss

GENERAL KNOWLEDGE

7 What was the name of the dog in the 'Famous Five' stories by Enid Blyton?

a) Lassie
b) Timmy
c) Scooby-Do

8 Can you connect these famous football teams with the grounds at which they play?

Chelsea
Manchester United
Tottenham Hotspur
Leeds United
Liverpool

White Hart Lane
Anfield
Stamford Bridge
Old Trafford
Elland Road

9 What is the name of an eagle's nest?

a) An eyrie
b) A spooky
c) Home Sweet Home

10 Which famous cartoon character hates Mondays and loves lasagne?

a) Popeye
b) Snoopy
c) Garfield

11 Lego, the building toy, got its name from the inventor's children who fought over the first set, shouting 'Lego! Let go! Leggo!'

True?
False?

12 Which composer was deaf for much of his later life and could not hear a note of the music he wrote?

a) Mozart
b) Beethoven
c) Verdi

GiMMe A B...!

BAZ AND SHARON'S SPECIAL WORD PUZZLE

Baz and Sharon are trying to find how many words they can make from the letters in the word Beaver. Would you like to help them? Start by solving the clues and writing your answers in the spaces provided.

B E A V E R

1 A buzzing insect that makes honey.

_____

4 Polar, Grizzly and Paddington are all of one of these!

_____

2 It's on the side of your head and you use it for listening.

_____

5 This sounds the same as No 4, but means to have no clothes on!

_____

3 These are made of iron and fitted across prison windows.

_____

6 Dad's favourite drink, sold in pints at the pub.

_____

Now can you find any more words of your own from the letters of the word BEAVER?

A new tale for bedtime or at the end of a Beaver Colony Meeting

MRS OUTSIDE AND MRS INSIDE

listen to stories

Mrs Outside and Mrs Inside lived in a little house on the outskirts of town. Mrs Outside loved gardening. Every day, rain or shine, she was outside, working in the garden.

"I can't wait to get out there today," she said at breakfast one morning. "I've got to prune my roses, dig the vegetable patch and get all those nasty weeds out of the flowerbed by the fence."

"Don't overdo it, dear," advised Mrs Inside.

"I won't," promised Mrs Outside.

Mrs Inside, on the other hand, loved housework. She spent every waking moment indoors, cleaning the house. "I'm looking forward to today, too," she added at breakfast. "I'm going to wash the kitchen floor, vacuum the sitting-room and wash all the net curtains in the house."

"Don't you overdo it, dear," warned Mrs Outside.

"I won't," promised Mrs Inside.

Life for Mrs Outside and Mrs Inside went on like this for many years. Then, one day, something very strange happened. "I don't feel like gardening today," sighed Mrs Outside.

"How funny you should say that," replied Mrs Inside. "I don't feel like doing any housework today." The two old ladies decided that they were tired of doing exactly the same things day after day. So they decided to swap!

Wearing Mrs Outside's gardening gloves and wellington boots, Mrs Inside went outside to work in the garden. The trouble was, of course, that Mrs Inside had not done any gardening for ages and did not know what she was doing!

"I'll pull up these weeds," she said, yanking some small green plants from a border.

"Those aren't weeds!" yelled Mrs Outside. "They're my best bedding plants!"

"Sorry," said Mrs Outside, turning on the hosepipe. "I'll water the hanging baskets instead.'

Poor Mrs Inside did not realise that the hose was the latest, high-jet squirter. It wriggled about in her hand like a huge live snake and sent a stream of water right into Mrs Outside's face.

"Gaah!" she spluttered.

"Sorry!" said Mrs Inside, again.

After such a terrible time in the garden, Mrs Inside went indoors for a sit-down. Mrs Outside followed her, ready to get on with the housework. Oh, dear! Mrs Outside had not done any cleaning or polishing for many years, either. She beat the dust out of the cushions, sending a cloud all over Mrs Inside and making her cough. The she polished the sideboard and knocked over a vase. Crash!

It landed beside Mrs Inside, making her leap out of her chair. And, finally, Mrs Outside rammed her friend's toes with the vacuum cleaner, making her yell and hop around like a kangaroo.
"Sorry!" said Mrs Outside as well.

Now Mrs Outside and Mrs Inside did not know what to do. Neither of them knew whether they wanted to be outside or inside!
"What shall we do?" asked Mrs Outside.
"I've no idea!" replied Mrs Inside.

The problem, was solved for the two old ladies when a letter arrived one morning. It told them that they had won some money on the Lottery.
"I know what we can spend it on," cried Mrs Inside.
"So do I!" chuckled Mrs Outside.

A few weeks later, the builders finished putting up a huge conservatory. The new room at the back of the house, made of plastic and glass, almost covered the garden. Mrs Outside and Mrs Inside filled it with carpets, curtains and lots of pretty indoor plants.
"Now I can be outside and inside at the same time," giggled Mrs Outside.
"And I can be inside and outside at the same time, too!" laughed Mrs Inside.

AND THEY BOTH LIVED HAPPILY EVER AFTER!

The holidays have just begun -
Rupert and Algy plan some fun . . .

They pack their rucksacks full, then take
A two-man tent towards the lake.

"This way!" says Algy as he sees
The boathouse in amongst the trees.

"Hurrah!" cries Rupert. "Here's our boat!
Let's clear her out and get afloat . . ."

and the **Raft**

The two pals stow their tent below,
Then clamber in - all set to go . . .

They paddle off without delay -
"Good! Now we're really underway!"

"There's Bingo!" Algy calls. "What's he
So busy making now? Let's see . . ."

Their chum explains he wants to make
A raft to sail on Nutwood's lake.

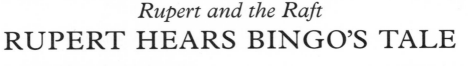

*"The first one I made looked just right
But then it vanished in the night!"*

*"The next day, all that I could find
Was this old rope it left behind . . ."*

*The pals tell Bingo they'll look out
For his raft, if it's still about.*

*They turn off from the lake and then
Resume their journey once again . . .*

*"We need to find a camping site . . .
I think that grassy bank looks right."*

*"It's perfect!" Algy smiles. "Now we
Can pitch our tent and cook some tea."*

He sets to work and soon the pair
Have supper in the open air.

"Let's check the map now, so we know
Exactly which way we should go."

Next morning, Rupert wakes to hear
A strange sound come from somewhere near . . .

He peers outside the tent and blinks
"It's frogs! They're everywhere!" he thinks.

As Algy steps outside they all
Crowd round . . . More frogs take up the call!

Then, suddenly, the croaking ends -
A big frog comes towards the friends . . .

"Hello!" the frog declares. "I bring
An urgent summons from our King!"

"He needs your help. Please follow me.
I'll lead you to His Majesty . . ."

The pals set off along the shore
But can't guess where they're heading for . . .

"The King's Apartments are not far
But only frogs know where they are!"

As Rupert walks along he sees
A lily pond, fringed by tall trees.

"This way!" the frog calls. "We can take
The floating path across the lake . . ."

Although the two chums hesitate
The lily pads can bear their weight!

The willows part and now the pair
Can see the Frog King sitting there . . .

The Frog King greets his guests. "Thank you
For coming when I asked you to . . ."

"I need your help to find out why
The source of Nutwood's lake's run dry!"

"This marker pole is how we know
The water level's falling low . . ."

"It's got so bad I fear that we
Are faced with a catastrophe!"

The two pals tell the King that they
Will find out what's wrong straightaway.

The frogs who guide the chums all seem
To think the problem lies upstream . . .

With every step the level sinks –
"It's getting lower!" Algy blinks.

"The water has a single source
From which the river runs its course . . ."

"A torrent used to fill this bed –
Now just a trickle flows instead!"

Ahead of them, the two pals see
An obstacle – what can it be?

RUPERT UNBLOCKS THE STREAM

"A gate!" cries Algy. "Somebody
Has blocked the flow deliberately!"

"It looks more like a capsized craft!"
The Messenger declares. "A raft?"

"It's Bingo's!" Rupert cries. "I'm sure -
The lost raft that he made before!"

"The mystery's over! Now we know
Why Nutwood's river's ceased to flow . . ."

The two pals lift the raft which blocks
The dammed up river from the rocks.

The frog lets out a joyful cry
To see the water rushing by . . .

"Let's see if Bingo's raft will take
Us back downstream to Nutwood's lake . . ."

"We're off now! Hold tight everyone!"
Calls Algy to the frogs. "What fun!"

The pals' plan works - soon they can see
The Frog King's mighty willow tree . . .

"The river's back to normal now!
You two have saved the day - but how?"

The Frog King marvels as he hears
The two pals' tale. "Well done!" he cheers.

He thanks the chums, "Without you two
We'd never have known what to do!"

The frogs all gather round and say
They'll help the pals' raft on its way . . .

Before long, Algy spots the place
Where they turned off from the main race.

The raft drifts on downstream and then
The two pals spot their tent again . . .

They thank the frogs and jump ashore -
Delighted to be back once more.

"Look!" Algy gives a startled cry -
The chums spot Bingo floating by . . .

"You've found my raft!" he blinks. "But where . . ."
"It's quite a story!" laugh the pair.

Read Rupert every day in the Daily Express

81

DON'T YOU HAVE HOMES TO GO TO?

Darren is a beaver, so the proper name for his home is a Lodge. How many other animal homes do you know?

Draw a line with a pencil or just your finger to connect these animals with their homes. One of them does not have a home - so connect the homeless odd-one-out with its mother!

BEE	STY
RABBIT	NEST
HORSE	SHEEP
LION	HIVE
PIG	WARREN
LAMB	STABLE
WASP	DEN

ANSWERS Bee hive   Rabbit warren   Horse stable   Lion den   Pig sty   Wasp nest   Lamb is homeless and goes with its mother, sheep.

So you'd like to know how to make . . .

PAINTED POTS

Here's your step-by-step guide to make them . . .

These decorated flowerpots are easy to make - and, if you fill them with bulbs or a flowering plant, they make a wonderful present to give to a friend or member of your family.

WARNING This item includes the use of varnish. Make sure a grown-up is with you during this part of the make - varnish gives off dangerous fumes and the windows must be open to let them out. Also, varnish needs to be removed with white spirit, so don't try to wash your brush in water or it will just go gooey and then set hard!

ARTIST BADGE

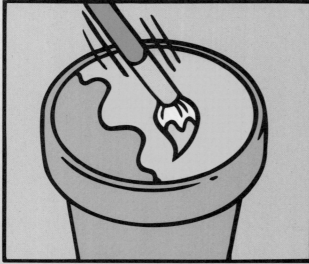

1. Begin by painting the inside of the flowerpot. Just use one plain colour. Leave to dry.

2. Now paint the rim round the top of the flowerpot in a different plain colour. Allow this to dry, too.

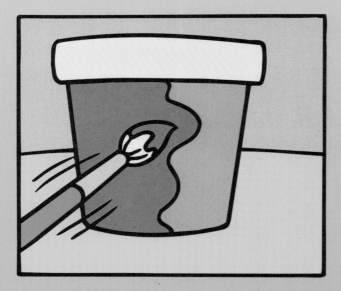

3. Complete the painting of the flowerpot in flat colour by covering the rest of the outside. Chose a colour that contrasts with the rim. Allow to dry.

4. Using a thinner brush, decorate the areas of flat colour with zig-zags, dots, squiggles and stripes. Make up any pattern you wish - the brighter the better! Allow to dry.

5. Time to varnish. Brush the coloured flowerpot all over with the clear varnish. Avoid brushing too heavily in case it makes the colours run and don't use too much varnish or it will run into ugly rivers and blobs. Leave to dry until not at all sticky to touch.

6. Now fill your finished flowerpot with some earth from the garden or, better still, a little potting compost.

7. Finally, plant some bulbs in the soil. If you can't wait or your present is needed urgently, plant a flower that is already in bloom to complete your pretty gift.

KNOCK, KNOCK!
WHO'S THERE?
SHIRLEY!
SHIRLEY WHO?
SHIRLEY you know my name by now!

Did you hear the story about the dust-carts?
YES, IT'S A LOAD OF RUBBISH!

What should you do if you break your leg in two places?
Never go back to those two places!

I SAY, WAITER! YOU'VE GOT YOUR THUMB IN MY SOUP.
It's okay, sir. It's not hot!

WHY ARE DOGS LIKE TREES?
Because they both have barks!

If crocodile skin makes expensive shoes, what does banana skin make?
SLIPPERS!

What did the spooky sentry say at the gate of the haunted castle?
Who ghosts there?

ENTERTAINER BADGE

TONGUE-TWISTERS TO MAKE YOUR FRIENDS GROAN!

HAVE YOU READ THESE BOOKS?

Animals with long necks by G Raffe

Windy days by Gail Force

How to avoid being late by Justin Time

DOCTOR, DOCTOR!
I keep thinking I'm a ladder!
I can cure you... but we'll have to take it one step at a time!

ANGRY CUSTOMER:
I want my money back for this TENNIS RACKET!
ASSISTANT IN SPORTS SHOP:
What's wrong with it, sir?
ANGRY CUSTOMER: Every time I hit the ball with it, it goes out!

HAVE YOU EVER SEEN A MAN-EATING TIGER?
No, but I saw the woman next door eating chicken!

TONGUE TWISTER -
RED LORRY, YELLOW LORRY

Why was the girl from Ancient Egypt feeling confused?
Because her Daddy was a **MUMMY!**

PHOTO FUN

"Do I have to salute like this for long?
My ice-lolly's dripping down my shirt!"

"It was a very late night last night –
the tent wouldn't shut up. So maybe
have fo

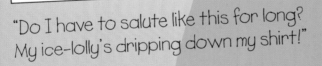

"I don't mind
admitting it –
I'm lost! Completely,
utterly and
hopelessly lost!"

Photo: Dave Wood

"Let's pretend we're on 'Gladiators'. **I'm Wolf**... who are you?"

Photo: Chris Boardman

"I thought the Animal Lover badge would be a sew on."

Photo: Chris Boardman

follow themes

MESSING ABOUT ON THE RIVER

Being Beavers as well as Beaver Scouts, Sharon and Baz feel very at home on the water. So they're trying their hand at canoeing.

Join the dots to draw in the outline of their boat. Then colour the rest of the picture with your crayons or felt-pens.

THE THREE BEAVERS IN

TOY TROUBLE

Sharon's Auntie Susan had a special job at the local factory. She ran the crêche. This was a nursery inside the factory where mothers and fathers could leave their young children while they were at work. As you can imagine, it was a very busy place!

One day, Sharon went to help Auntie Susan at the crêche. "It's very good of you to give up your time like this, Sharon," said Auntie Susan with a big smile.
"That's okay, Auntie," laughed Sharon in reply. "Beaver Scouts like me enjoy meeting new people and helping out."

Sharon's first job was to put out all the toys. Then, when the children arrived, she joined in as they played with the toys. "How are you getting on?" asked her aunt as she passed by.
"This isn't work," giggled Sharon. "It's fun!"

Later, the kind young Beaver helped to serve orange and biscuits before going back to playing with her new little friends. The time just flew by and, before Sharon knew it, it was time to go home.

"You've been a great help," cried Auntie Susan, patting her niece on the back, "And all the grown-ups are so grateful that they've been able to work in peace." "Can I come back another day?" asked Sharon, eagerly.

Later that day, it was time for the weekly meeting of the 1st Pedigree Beaver Scout Colony. As usual, Sharon was the first to arrive. "Would you move Archie for me, Sharon?" asked the Beaver Scout Leader. "We're playing games this evening and he'll be in the way."

Archie was the Colony mascot - a huge, soft-toy beaver with big teeth and a long tail. Sharon sat Archie in the corner of the hut. But, when the games began and everyone was running and jumping on the wooden floor, Archie fell over the his big tail stuck out sideways.

"WHOOPS!" yelled Sharon, as she ran round the room and tripped over Archie's tail. The big toy was proving to be a nuisance!

Then Baz arrived at the meeting a few minutes late. He had been shopping with his Mum and spent his birthday money on a new toy. "Look at this," he chuckled, proudly. "Isn't he cool!" Baz left his new toy sitting on one of the hall chairs as he joined in the games. But everyone wanted to play Musical Chairs and, as the game was set up, the chair on which Baz's soldier doll was sitting was snatched up. Crash! The new toy fell to the floor and came to pieces. "Baz's doll is in the way, too!" murmured Sharon

Meanwhile, outside, Darren was waiting for his two friends to finish their Colony meeting so he could walk home with them. He sat on a bench with Gus, his favourite teddy, sitting next to him. "Won't be long now, Gus," chuckled the little Beaver.

Suddenly, a heavy lorry thundered past and its giant tyre splashed through a puddle in the gutter. Splash! Splat! Baz's best teddy was plastered with mud and dirty water. "I'm going to tell Baz and Sharon," wailed Darren, hurrying into the hut.

Daz's accident with Gus was the last straw for Sharon. "All these toys are stopping us getting on with our Beaver Scout meeting," she told the Beaver Leader. "So I'm going to do something about it!" When the next meeting took place, the Beavers in Sharon's colony found that one corner of the hut had been set aside for a special purpose. It was a crêche - for their toys!

"Leave your dolls, teddies and toys with me," laughed Sharon, "and I will look after them properly while you're all busy. Then you can pick them up when it's time to go home."

Everyone was happy to leave their toys with Sharon and the two boys, Baz and Daz, helped her to look after the visitors. Sharon's Beaver Colony crêche was a great success. "I can't wait to tell Auntie Susan," giggled Sharon.

SPECIAL FEATURE

BOY AND GIRL RACERS

Here's an exciting subject you've probably never heard of - Classic Pedal Cars and Pedal Car Racing ...

THE AUSTIN JUNIOR J40

The Austin Junior J40 Pedal Car was first made in 1949. Based on a real car, the Austin A40 Devon and Dorset, this mini-version for children was built at a special factory in South Wales. Employing injured miners and using left-over metal from the main Austin factory, the Austin Junior Car Factory turned out 32,098 J40 pedal cars by the time production stopped in 1971.

1.6 metres long, 0.69 metres high and weighing 43 kilograms, the J40 was a well-made and expensive toy. It had real working headlights and horn, proper tyres, a realistic-looking dashboard and leather cloth seats. It also had a bonnet and boot that opened and lots of shiny chrome. Owning one felt like owning your own proper little car!

THE PATHFINDER

As well as the J40, the pedal car factory also made a smaller number of Pathfinder Specials. Where the J40 was based on a road car, the Pathfinder was a small version of an Austin Seven racing car. So it looked sleeker and more sporty.

Both the J40 and the Pathfinder have delighted generations of children. They have been used to teach road safety in schools and appear in many old road safety films. Others have found homes fitted to roundabouts at fairs. These were often changed so that they had two steering wheels, side by side, and no pedals. Recently, however, these lovely old toys have been put to a new use - Pedal Car Racing!

ROAD SAFETY
BADGE

96

A J40 with the real car it was based on, the Austin A40

GLORIOUS GAYDON

On September 26th 1999, young pedal car racers from all over the country arrived at Gaydon near Stratford-upon-Avon for the National Pedal Car Rally. Celebrating the 50th year of these little machines, the boy and girl racers competed in a number of speed races, long-distance races and driving tests. As you can see from the photographs, great fun was had by all and there were a great many tired and aching legs on the way home that night!

If you would like to own a classic pedal car, or become involved in children's pedal car racing, you can contact the secretary of the Pedal Car Club by phoning:

01527 876293 (after 6pm please).

Alternatively, for further information, contact Rob Stuart's Internet website: http://www.austinworks.com/pedalcar.html.

Information and photographs kindly supplied by the Austin J40 Pedal Car Club. All photographs by Rayne Williams.

97

Learning new skills and having fun ...

EARWiGS, and EGGY

Camping is the highlight of the Scouting year and the main reason why many youngsters join the Movement in the first place. Whether you go on a Family Camp with the Beavers, or to a Cub Camp or Pack Holiday with the Cubs, you are sure to have a WONDERFUL time!

There is always so much to see, so much to do and so much to learn. And nothing beats the thrill of living in the great outdoors! As with everything you do as a Scout, there is a right way and a wrong way to go about it. So here are some useful tips and handy hints to help you enjoy the summer camp to the full...

CAMPER
BADGE

EXCITEMENT BREAD

SOME THINGS TO REMEMBER

Make sure that everything you take to camp is marked clearly with you name. Otherwise you'll lose it! Remember to take some plastic bags with you. They are extremely useful for storing wet and dirty clothes and stopping them spoiling your clean ones.

Try to pack your bag yourself. Remember - you will have to do it on your own when you come back from camp. The best method is to lay everything out on your bedroom floor and then fold everything tightly so it fits easily. Another good idea is to put the things you might need on the journey in the side pockets of your rucksack. Then you can get at the easily. Be prepared for the journey to camp. It may take a long time and, once the first excitement of being underway is over, you could be bored. So have some travel-games ready. Try to be as thoughtful and helpful as you can at camp. Remember - the more you put into your time there, the more you get out. And when it is all over, take everything home with you. The golden rule of camping is:

LEAVE ONLY ONE THING BEHIND - YOUR THANKS!

And this is what you have to do:

1. With other Cub Scouts, camp under canvas for at least three nights (not necessary on the same occasion).

2. Help pack your kit for a Cub Scout camp.

3. Help pitch and strike a tent and know how to care for it.

4. At camp, help to prepare, cook, serve and clear away a meal if possible out of doors.

5. Know the basic health and safety rules for camp and how to prepare for tent inspection.

6. Take part in at least one of the following activities while at camp:
   a) Campfire
   b) Scout's own
   c) Wide Game
   d) Joint activity with other Cub Scouts on site or from a local group
   e) A Good Turn for the site
   f) Any suitable similar activity
   g) Help to tidy up the campsite before you leave

CAMPER BADGE

Don't forget, if you are a Cub Scout, you can gain an activity Badge for being at camp. Here's what the badge looks like:

INTERESTING INFO.

The first ever organised camp was run by the founder of the scout movement, Lord Baden-Powell, at Brownsea Island in Pool Harbour, Dorset, in 1907. Although the boys were not true scouts in the modern sense of the word, they did all the things that modern scouts enjoy doing. The site is now looked after by The National Trust and you can go there to visit (or even to camp) if you wish.

And finally - DON'T FORGET THE EGGYBREAD! Scout's have enjoyed this delicious treat at camp for generations. The recipe: Break some eggs into a bowl and whisk them up with a fork. Dip a slice of bread in the runny mixture. Fry the egg-coated bread in a frying-pan until crisp and golden. You haven't really been to camp until you've had your eggy-bread!

IT'S FUN OUTDOORS!

Dear Beaver Scouts,

Akela has been telling us at our Sixer's Meeting that some of you will be swimming up to join us in the Pack soon and she suggested that we should write to tell you a bit about what we do.

Our favourite bit is when we go on Pack Holiday or to camp. A Pack Holiday is when some or all of the Cub Scouts go away for a weekend together.

When we get there it's great fun because you can do lots of things that you can't do in your meeting place. Akela lets the older Cub Scouts camp out so that they can earn their Camper Activity Badge whilst the younger Cub Scouts can sleep indoors.

We remember our first Pack Holiday because we had to dress up as Spacemen who had landed on another planet. When we landed we were given some canes to build a shelter with. We worked together in a Six and Baloo (another Leader) helped us to collect ferns and grasses to make a roof. When we built it we had to test to see if it was waterproof. Our Sixer told us to sit in the shelter and she would pour water onto the roof. Guess what? It wasn't waterproof and we got wet!

Another activity we did was to cook twists over a campfire's embers. Akela kept a careful eye on us to see that we were safe. We had to make some dough and wrap it around a green stick. Then we held the sticks over the embers (that's when the fire is dying down) and waited for the dough to turn brown. Then Akela said we could eat them. Well we didn't like the look of ours at first but we closed our eyes and bit into them. They were delicious! We couldn't wait to have another bite. Akela let us all make another one as well but no more as she said we wouldn't eat our dinners up.

When you join our Pack we hope you will have as much fun at your first Pack Holiday as we did.

Bye for now
Gus, Jane, Ice, Joe, Brenda and Sammy

like to
think

PRIVATE THOUGHTS

"If he asks me to hold this up any higher, gonna burn my nos

Photo: R Al

"You must be kidding! I'm not going in that group for today's hike - **they're all girls!**"

"I'm not thinking anything much right now ... **except this lolly's nice!**"

"Shall I join this football game or not? They're all boys... but they're all rubbish!"

"I know the food at camp isn't much cop, but this is ridiculous!"
Photo: Peter Baker

103

WHAT A CLEAN-UP

There are six painting rollers hidden in the picture. Can you find them all?

HANDYMAN BADGE

The three Beavers...